TROUBLED WATERS

D. DAVID C. CUADRA & R. MIEL

At the 30th International Comic Strip Festival in Angoulême (23-26 January 2003), the European Parliament received the Alph-Art Communication prize for its 'Troubled Waters' album, judged to be 'best communication campaign using the comic strip medium'.

Although the adventures portrayed in this story are entirely fictional, the procedures described accurately reflect reality.

Editor-in-chief: Directorate-General Information and Public Relations of the European Parliament (Publications and Events – Jacques Hinckxt)

Concept and production: Concerto, Brussels – www.concerto.be
Writers: Cristina Cuadra, Rudi Miel
Illustration: Dominique David
Colours: Etienne Simon

Strasbourg Buildings: Architecture Studio

Thanks to Marta Kindelán Bustelo and Bibliothèque Solvay

See the European Parliament website
www.europarl.eu.int

...and those of its British and Irish Offices:

www.europarl.org.uk

www.europarl.ie

UPDATE 2006

***Page - 2 - :**

Second Paragraph
(...) although the adventures portrayed in this story are entirely fictional, the legislative procedures described accurately reflect reality (...)

Eighth Paragraph
See the European Parliament website
www.europarl.europa.eu

***Page - 36 - :**

Second paragraph: The European Union
The European Union is an ever closer union between the nations of Europe. Its Member States fly their flags in Strasbourg. The twenty five Member States – soon to be more – adopt common policies and measures, because they can achieve better results together than they could individually.

Forth paragraph: If I don`t...
The European Parliament, which MEP Irina Vega here refers to as 'Parliament', is elected every five years, by universal suffrage of the citizens of the Member States of the European Union. At present the European Parliament has 732 Members and since September 2005, 18 Bulgarian and 35 Romanian observers.

*** Page - 37- :**

Second paragraph: Environment Committee
Members of the European Parliament are divided among 20 parliamentary standing committees; the Environment Committee is one of them.

Forth paragraph: Commission
The European Commission (here referred to simply as 'the Commission') is the institution which initiates 'Community laws', manages European policies and enforces the treaties. At present it is made up of 25 independent Commissioners (one for each Member States).

QA-45-02-224-EN-K

UPDATE 2006

***Page - 2 - :**

Second Paragraph
(...) although the adventures portrayed in this story are entirely fictional, the legislative procedures described accurately reflect reality (...)

Eighth Paragraph
See the European Parliament website
www.europarl.europa.eu

***Page - 36 - :**

Second paragraph: The European Union
The European Union is an ever closer union between the nations of Europe. Its Member States fly their flags in Strasbourg. The twenty five Member States – soon to be more – adopt common policies and measures, because they can achieve better results together than they could individually.

Forth paragraph: If I don`t...
The European Parliament, which MEP Irina Vega here refers to as 'Parliament', is elected every five years, by universal suffrage of the citizens of the Member States of the European Union. At present the European Parliament has 732 Members and since September 2005, 18 Bulgarian and 35 Romanian observers.

*** Page - 37- :**

Second paragraph: Environment Committee
Members of the European Parliament are divided among 20 parliamentary standing committees; the Environment Committee is one of them.

Forth paragraph: Commission
The European Commission (here referred to simply as 'the Commission') is the institution which initiates 'Community laws', manages European policies and enforces the treaties. At present it is made up of 25 independent Commissioners (one for each Member States).

QA-45-02-224-EN-K

I HOPE IT'S QUIETER THAN LAST NIGHT ...
KEEP YOUR EYES PEELED!

STOP
...TWO FALSE ALARMS IN THE SOUTH SECTION IN LESS THAN AN HOUR!

CHEERS, MAX, SEE YOU TOMORROW!

WEEEE

WAH
WAH

NOT THE SOUTH SECTION AGAIN!

1

THE PLENARY TODAY WILL BE CRUCIAL ...
IF I DON'T MANAGE TO WIN PARLIAMENT OVER WE'LL HAVE MISSED A WONDERFUL OPPORTUNITY TO USE OUR ENVIRONMENTAL POWERS ...

... AND IT'S THE FATE OF FUTURE GENERATIONS THAT'S AT STAKE – AND OF THE WHOLE PLANET!

A FEW YEARS FROM NOW A GLASS OF WATER LIKE THIS COULD BE A LUXURY, IF POLITICIANS CAN'T AGREE ON A WAY TO PROTECT OUR WATER SUPPLIES.

YES, **SOLIDARITY** IS THE ONLY ANSWER. THANKS.

RRING

IT'S OK. I'LL ANSWER IT. TIME'S GETTING ON.

GOOD MORNING, MR SORO. YES, MS VEGA'S STILL HERE, BUT SHE'S DUE IN THE CHAMBER VERY SOON... CAN I HELP YOU? IS IT URGENT?

YES, CHRIS... YOUR GROUP'S VOTING WITH US? **THAT'S GREAT NEWS!** LET'S HOPE THE REST OF THEM DO THE SAME!

IRINA! I HEAR THE ENVIRONMENT COMMITTEE'S MADE YOU ITS RAPPORTEUR FOR THE WATER DIRECTIVE! I'M SURE WE CAN RELY ON YOU TO POUR OIL ON TROUBLED WATERS! **HA! HA!**
YOU CAN LAUGH! WAIT UNTIL YOU'VE SEEN MY AMENDMENTS TO THE COMMISSION PROPOSAL!

BE CAREFUL, IRINA. THERE ARE A LOT OF INTERESTS AT STAKE!
THERE ARE INDEED. AND THEY ALL HAVE TO BE RECONCILED.

YOU'RE AN INNOCENT, IRINA. A DREAMER...
TRUST ME!

3

WATER IS NOT A COMMERCIAL PRODUCT LIKE ANY OTHER, ...
L'EAU N'EST PAS UN BIEN MARCHAND ...
EL AGUA NO ES UN BIEN...
...EN ALMINDELIG HANDELSVARE...
...SONDERN EIN ERERBTES GUT...
... PRODOTTO COMMERCIALE...
... NÃO É UM PRODUTO COMERCIAL...
TO NEPO ΔEN EINAI...
...WATER IS GEEN GEWONE...
VESI EI OLE ...
VATTEN ÄR INGEN...
...IT IS THE HERITAGE OF ...
Italiano
Nederlands

... THE PEOPLE OF THE EUROPEAN UNION!
88
89

FOR ONCE WE ALL AGREE...
395
396

...AND CO-DECISION WITH THE COUNCIL OF MINISTERS APPLIES!

LADIES AND GENTLEMEN, WE SHALL NOW VOTE!

LADIES AND GENTLEMEN, PARLIAMENT HAS VOTED UNANIMOUSLY ...
...IN FAVOUR OF EUROPE'S CITIZENS BEING FULLY INVOLVED IN DECISION-MAKING ON WATER POLICY!
183
184
133

4

WELL DONE, IRINA. VERY PERSUASIVE!
WELL DONE, ALEX! WE MAKE A GREAT TEAM!

THERE ARE QUITE A FEW VISITORS TODAY. I'LL TRY AND GET A TABLE.
ARE YOU HAVING COFFEE?

PARLIAMENT HAS GOT A LOT TO SAY ABOUT WATER POLLUTION, TARIFFS, MANAGEMENT AND, ABOVE ALL, THE DEADLINES FOR IMPLEMENTING THESE MEASURES.
WE'LL BE GETTING THE COUNCIL'S COMMON POSITION SOON... THEN THINGS WILL START TO HOT UP!
BYE, EVERYONE. I'M OFF TO BRUSSELS.

AT THIS TIME OF NIGHT? YOU'LL GET HOME VERY LATE.
YES. I'VE GOT A CARPOOLING ARRANGEMENT WITH TWO COLLEAGUES.
I'M CATCHING THE TRAIN TOMORROW MORNING.

...NEW ENVIRONMENTAL DISASTER: THE CHEMICAL GROUP CARIMAS, THE CHIEF SUSPECT...
EUROPEAN VOICE

HOW DREADFUL! MORE TOXIC WASTE POURED INTO A RIVER. IF IT GOES ON LIKE THIS THERE SOON WON'T BE ANY CLEAN RIVERS LEFT IN EUROPE!

MESDAMES ET MESSIEURS, NOUS ARRIVONS À BRUXELLES-GARE DU LUXEMBOURG. DAMES EN HEREN...
THAT'S STRANGE ...I'VE GOT THE FEELING THAT GUY'S WATCHING ME...

5

I SEEM TO SPEND MY WHOLE LIFE ON THE TRAIN BETWEEN BRUSSELS AND STRASBOURG ...

...BUT I'D HATE TO HAVE TO CHOOSE BETWEEN MUSSELS AND CHIPS AND STRASBOURG ONION TART!

MY GOODNESS, WHAT A WIND!
HELP!

info
info

?!
BUT ...

6

A FEW WEEKS LATER...
AH, THE MEETING'S STARTING AT NINE, AS PLANNED.

ALEX! HOW ARE YOU? HAVEN'T SEEN YOU FOR AGES! I THOUGHT YOU'D DISAPPEARED.
MARTHA!...

...VERY NEARLY. I HAVEN'T GOT TIME FOR BREAKFAST ...
ARE YOU GOING MY WAY?

STILL WORKING HARD FOR THE ENVIRONMENT COMMITTEE?
YES. AND WHAT ABOUT YOU? WEREN'T YOU OFF TO CHECHNYA WITH THE OSCE?

IF I COULD JUST REMIND YOU OF THE AGENDA: FIRST WE SHALL CONSIDER THE EPP GROUP'S QUESTIONS ON AIRCRAFT NOISE... THEN WE'LL MOVE ON TO THE SOCIALIST GROUP'S QUESTIONS ON THE DRAFT DIRECTIVE ON GMOs.

MR PRADO.

IN OUR OPINION AIRCRAFT NOISE AROUND AIRPORTS SHOULD BE STOPPED ...

...BY BANNING LOW FLYING OVER TOWNS PRIOR TO LANDING.

MS VEGA?
ANY BAN MUST TAKE ACCOUNT OF AIRCRAFT SAFETY ...

7

...WE ALL KNOW THAT CLIMATIC CONDITIONS SOMETIMES MEAN THAT ROUTES HAVE TO BE CHANGED. AND THE IMPACT ON LOCAL EMPLOYMENT AND REGIONAL DEVELOPMENT WOULD ALSO HAVE TO BE LOOKED AT.

I'M SORRY, MR PRADO. YOU'VE ALREADY SPOKEN. WE MUST MOVE ON TO THE NEXT ITEM ON THE AGENDA ...

WHAT ABOUT A PIZZA AT **DA MIMO**?
Jean Monnet
GOOD IDEA! SOME FRESH AIR WOULD DO US GOOD ...

DA MIMO
PIZZERIA
Jupiter
ENJOYING THE SUN?
JACQUES! HOW LOVELY!
I'VE TRIED TO PHONE YOU, BUT THERE WAS NO REPLY...

I'M WORKING FLAT OUT. I'M DOING ANOTHER PHOTO EXHIBITION, NOT FAR FROM HERE.
TARIF
THAT'S GREAT! WHERE?

AT THE BIBLIOTHÈQUE SOLVAY... THE SUBJECT SHOULD INTEREST YOU. IT'S CALLED **'TROUBLED WATERS'**.
FANTASTIC!
BEPPI, UNA NAPOLITANA E DUE FRUTTI DI MARE!

SIGNORE?
NOTHING, THANK YOU.
POLICE
YOU WON'T STAY AND EAT WITH US?

8

SOME OTHER TIME... I'VE GOT TO GET BACK TO THE LAB!
STRAIGHT AWAY?
YES ... OTHERWISE
I'LL GET ANOTHER PARKING TICKET!
SHALL WE CALL?
COME AND EAT AT MY HOUSE!
I'M CELEBRATING THE EXHIBITION WITH A FEW FRIENDS.
POLICE

Altiero Spinelli
60
THANK YOU, MS VEGA.

ALEX? I'VE GOT THE COUNCIL COMMON POSITION ON THE NEW COMMISSION PROPOSAL!
ALREADY ?

HERE WE GO AGAIN THEN?
YES, WE'VE GOT TO GET READY FOR THE SECOND READING IN PARLIAMENT.

ALEX, I'M RELYING ON YOU. GET ALL THE INFORMATION YOU CAN LAY YOUR HANDS ON: LISTS OF POLLUTANTS, CURRENT LEGISLATION IN THE MEMBER STATES, EXISTING CONTROLS, ETC... I WANT ALL THE BACKGROUND WE CAN GET FOR MY AMENDMENTS TO THE COUNCIL POSITION.
YES, MA'AM!

9

DIANA WORKS FOR A HUMAN RIGHTS **NGO.**
AND YOU'RE WORKING ON THE ENVIRONMENT?
YES, AMONG OTHER THINGS.
AH! KOSTAS! THIS IS IRINA, THE FRIEND I TOLD YOU ABOUT...

...WHO'S A MEMBER OF THE EUROPEAN PARLIAMENT.
PLEASED TO MEET YOU. ARE YOU A PHOTOGRAPHER TOO?
YES, I'M ALSO INTERESTED IN THE EFFECT MAN IS HAVING ON THE LANDSCAPE...

... BUT MY PHOTOS HAVEN'T MADE THE FRONT PAGE YET!
THAT PHOTO OF CARIMAS THAT WAS IN THE PAPERS – WAS IT ONE OF YOURS, JACQUES?
YES, LOOK ...

...AND I'VE GOT SOME MORE. I'LL GIVE YOU A PREVIEW, IF YOU LIKE...
THEY'RE GOING IN THE EXHIBITION.

HAVE YOU SEEN THIS ONE?!
BURST DAM CONTAINING WATER CONTAMINATED WITH SULPHURIC ACID NEAR A LEAD MINE IN SOUTHERN EUROPE.

RRRING

EXCUSE ME!

10

WHO ARE YOU? WHO'S PAYING YOU TO DO THIS? WHO'S BEHIND IT ALL?
YOU ARE FOND OF WATER, MR GOLDING. BUT CAN YOU SWIM?

YES, AND ESPECIALLY WELL AGAINST THE TIDE!

KLANK

THIS IS NOT THE FIRST TIME. I'VE BEEN GETTING THESE THREATS FOR THREE WEEKS.

OF COURSE. THERE ARE SOME VERY POWERFUL PEOPLE BEHIND THIS DUMPING BUSINESS.
YOU SHOULD TAKE IT SERIOUSLY, JACQUES.
PHOTOGRAPHY IS A HIGH-RISK PROFESSION!

HAVE YOU GOT ANY IDEA WHERE THESE THREATS ARE COMING FROM?
I'VE GOT NO DEFINITE PROOF, BUT I SUSPECT CARIMAS. WHO ELSE WOULD BE INTERESTED IN HUSHING UP THIS AFFAIR? YOU SHOULD BE CAREFUL TOO. I WOULDN'T BE SURPRISED IF THEY TRIED TO PUT PRESSURE ON THE POLITICIANS AS WELL.

MMM. IT'S STRANGE THOUGH ...

HEY! I'VE SEEN THAT GUY OVER THERE SOMEWHERE BEFORE ...

THE NEXT DAY...
CBT782

GOOD MORNING!

11

IRINA!
SOMEONE WHO CLAIMS TO HAVE CONFIDENTIAL INFORMATION ABOUT THE EFFLUENTS HAS BEEN TRYING TO CONTACT YOU. THEY KEEP GETTING CUT OFF, AS IF THEY WERE IN A PHONE BOX...

DID YOU KNOW THAT JACQUES HAS BEEN GETTING ANONYMOUS THREATS FOR DAYS?
WHY JACQUES?
BECAUSE HE TOOK THE PHOTOGRAPH THAT STARTED THE SCANDAL...

AND HE DIDN'T LEAVE A NAME?
NO. HE SEEMED VERY NERVOUS.

HAVE YOU GOT TODAY'S PAPERS?
I HAVEN'T HAD TIME TO LOOK ...

CARIMAS IN COURT!
...CHRISTIAN LOB, THE GROUP'S MANAGING DIRECTOR, ACCUSES THE PRESS OF MANIPULATION AND THREATENS TO PROSECUTE ANY PAPERS THAT PASS ON WHAT HE VIEWS AS LIBELLOUS ACCUSATIONS...

I DON'T THINK THEY'LL STOP AT THIS. THEY'LL TRY TO PUT ON MORE PRESSURE ...

RRiiNG

HELLO? NO, I'M SORRY, MS VEGA CAN'T ANSWER THAT QUESTION. NOT AT THIS STAGE.

IT WAS THE EUROPEAN POST. THEY WANTED A STATEMENT FROM YOU ON THE CARIMAS AFFAIR. THEY WERE DEMANDING TO KNOW IF THE WATER DIRECTIVE WOULD MAKE IT EASIER TO STOP PEOPLE FROM DUMPING TOXIC EFFLUENT.
WITH ALL THIS STRESS I'M NOT SURE IF I SHALL BE GOING TO THE WORKING DINNER TONIGHT.
RRiiNG
THE ONE BEING ORGANISED BY TERRA VIVA?

YES. THEY'VE INVITED PEOPLE FROM THE COMMISSION AND PARLIAMENT, AND REPRESENTATIVES OF INDUSTRY. AND SOME JOURNALISTS AND NGOS.
RRiiNG
THE GROUP MEETING WILL GO ON ALL MORNING. TAKE CARE OF THE PRESS, WILL YOU, AND DON'T LET YOURSELF BE INTIMIDATED. YOU'RE GOOD AT THIS KIND OF THING.
RRiiNG

12

MS?
VEGA...
HERE'S MY INVITATION.
GOOD EVENING, MS VEGA! FOLLOW ME, PLEASE. YOU HAVE A RESERVED SEAT NEXT TO MR OPDEBEEK, FROM FIMOIL.

I THINK WE HAVE TO BE FIRMER ABOUT THE DEADLINES FOR THE NEW IMPLEMENTATION MEASURES TO COME INTO FORCE. WE NEED TO GO BEYOND THE 'POLLUTER PAYS' PRINCIPLE. FINES AND TAXES ARE NOT ENOUGH TO STOP THE DAMAGE TO RIVERS AND GROUNDWATER.
I AGREE WITH MS VEGA. IT IS QUITE POSSIBLE FOR INDUSTRY TO RESTRUCTURE...

FIMOIL IS AN EXAMPLE. WE HAVE ADOPTED NEW ENVIRONMENTAL PROTECTION MEASURES ...

...WHICH CONSIST OF HAVING YOUR TOXIC WASTE SHIPPED 100 KMS TO SOMEONE ELSE'S LAND, AND DUMPING IT THERE!

THAT IS NOT TRUE! WE'VE UNDERGONE RIGOROUS TESTS WHICH PROVE THAT FIMOIL'S FACTORIES ARE CLEAN!

LADIES AND GENTLEMEN, THANK YOU FOR TAKING PART IN THIS ROUND TABLE DISCUSSION. MAY I REMIND YOU THAT THERE WILL BE ANOTHER MEETING SOON.
SAURUS

13

MS VEGA! I MUST SPEAK TO YOU! I CAN'T STAY HERE ANY LONGER. IT'S TOO RISKY!
YOU?!

YOU MUST LISTEN TO WHAT I'VE GOT TO SAY! I'VE BEEN TRYING TO SPEAK TO YOU FOR DAYS ...
I DON'T KNOW WHO YOU ARE OR WHY YOU'RE FOLLOWING ME, BUT I'VE GOT NO INTENTION OF LISTENING TO YOU ...
?

PLEASE! IT'S DANGEROUS FOR ME TO BE HERE!
!
IT'S ABOUT CARIMAS!

GET THESE SAMPLES ANALYSED...

...WE'LL TALK AGAIN LATER!

CLOSING TIME, LADIES AND GENTLEMEN...

14

WHAT?

YOU'RE NOT SERIOUSLY THINKING OF HAVING THEM ANALYSED?

WHAT WOULD YOU DO IN MY POSITION?

216

JACQUES? ARE YOU FREE THIS EVENING?... WILL YOU COME AND EAT AT MY PLACE? SOMETHING REALLY STRANGE HAPPENED TO ME YESTERDAY!...

...AND HE GAVE ME THESE TWO TEST TUBES...
ALL VERY STRANGE... SAMPLES... BUT SAMPLES OF WHAT?
I HAVEN'T GOT THE FAINTEST IDEA...

Sciences appliquées
Secrétariat porte B-Niv. 4
U
Sciences appliquées
Porte E
L
Ua

PERHAPS WE'LL FIND OUT WHAT'S REALLY GOING ON NOW...
I DON'T KNOW... IT'S PROBABLY JUST A JOKE IN RATHER POOR TASTE...

I'M NOT SO SURE... TAKE THEM TO A LAB TOMORROW! IT'S A RISK WE'LL HAVE TO TAKE ...

15

A FEW WEEKS LATER...
IT'S GOING TO BE A LONG DAY!

YOU'RE TELLING ME!
WE'VE GOT THE VOTE IN PLENARY ON MY AMENDMENTS TO THE COUNCIL COMMON POSIT-ION!... AND THERE ARE A LOT OF THEM!

THE ENVIRONMENT COMMITTEE SUPPORTED THEM ALL. YOU WEREN'T SURE THEY WOULD AGREE TO REDUCING THE IMPLEMENTATION DEADLINES FROM SIXTEEN TO TEN YEARS...

AND WE ARE ASKING FOR RADIOACTIVE SUBSTANCES TO BE INCLUDED! NEITHER THE COMMISSION NOR THE COUNCIL DID THAT!

WE WILL NOW VOTE ON AMENDMENT 66, UNDERGROUND WATER ...

479

16

HOW DOES THE EUROPEAN PARLIAMENT STAND ON THE IMPACT OF ITS DRAFT LAW ON THE CHEMICAL INDUSTRY?
WE'VE LISTENED TO THEIR ARGUMENTS. DISCUSSIONS ARE UNDER WAY. OUR AIM IS TO ACHIEVE A FAIR BALANCE. BUT WATER IS AN ESSENTIAL RESOURCE. AND WE'RE GOING TO PROTECT IT!

AND WHAT ABOUT THE DIFFERENCES OF OPINION BETWEEN YOU AND THE COUNCIL? WHEN WILL THE DIRECTIVE BE ADOPTED?
THE REPORT IS CURRENTLY ON ITS SECOND READING. SO WE HAVE TO REACH AGREEMENT WITH THE COUNCIL, IF NECESSARY VIA A CONCILIATION COMMITTEE. THANK YOU.

SIR, SIR... YOU ARE A MEMBER OF PARLIAMENT...
?!
HA! HA!
Paul-Henri Spaak

SEE YOU TOMORROW, 'HONORABLE MEMBER'... I'M STARVING!
HA, HA! DON'T GO TO THE CHIP SHOP IN PLACE JOURDAN. THEIR CHIPS ARE MUCH TOO GOOD!

Antoine

POLITIE
?

WHAT'S GOING ON, JACQUES?!
I'LL GIVE YOU ONE GUESS!

17

THEY'VE TAKEN SOME EQUIPMENT... AND NEGATIVES AND PRINTS AS WELL... IT'S GOING TO COST ME A FORTUNE!
THEY'VE SMASHED THE WHOLE PLACE UP!

YES. THEY TRIED REALLY HARD – BUT THEY WERE WASTING THEIR TIME!

THIS IS WHAT THEY WERE LOOKING FOR!

'THEY'?

I'M SURE! CARIMAS ARE THE ONES BEHIND THIS!
HAVE YOU TOLD THE POLICE?
I HAVEN'T GOT ANY PROOF, UNLESS YOU COUNT THE SCANDAL MY PHOTO CAUSED AND THE THREATS OVER THE PHONE.

WHAT A MESS! CARLA CALLED ME... I TOLD YOU YOU WERE TAKING A RISK! THESE PEOPLE DON'T CARE HOW MUCH DAMAGE THEY DO...
KOSTAS!
WE'VE FINISHED. WE'LL SEE YOU DOWN AT THE STATION FOR THE STATEMENT.

YOU CAN'T LET THIS GO UN-REPORTED. I'M GOING TO CALL YOUR PAPER ...
IT'S YOUR LAB I NEED... I'VE JUST GOT TIME TO REDO THE PRINTS BEFORE THE EXHIBITION.

MR GOLDING, DO YOU THINK THE BREAK-IN IS LINKED TO THE CARIMAS AFFAIR?

18

* Carimas in the hot seat again. Photographer Jacques Golding victim of an unexplained break-in. 19

* Faculty of applied sciences. Test results:

FOR SEVERAL YEARS THE CHEMICAL INDUSTRY HAS BEEN GOING THROUGH A CRISIS LINKED TO THE RESTRUCTURING OF CERTAIN SECTORS...
HELLO?
HAVE YOU GOT THE RESULTS?

WHO'S SPEAKING?
IT DOESN'T MATTER, IRINA! LOOK IN THE NOTES ON THE CARIMAS INQUIRY; YOU'LL FIND THE SAME CHEMICAL COMPONENTS THERE AS IN THE SAMPLES ...

AND WHAT... HELLO!? HELLO!?

HOW DID HE KNOW I GOT THE RESULTS TODAY?...

A WEEK LATER...
HAVE YOU INFORMED THE ADDRESSEE?

WE WERE WAITING FOR YOUR INSTRUCTIONS.

MS VEGA, WE INTERCEPTED A SUSPICIOUS PACKAGE ADDRESSED TO YOU THIS MORNING. CAN YOU COME DOWN TO THE MAIL ROOM?

YOU SEEM TO HAVE AN ADMIRER...

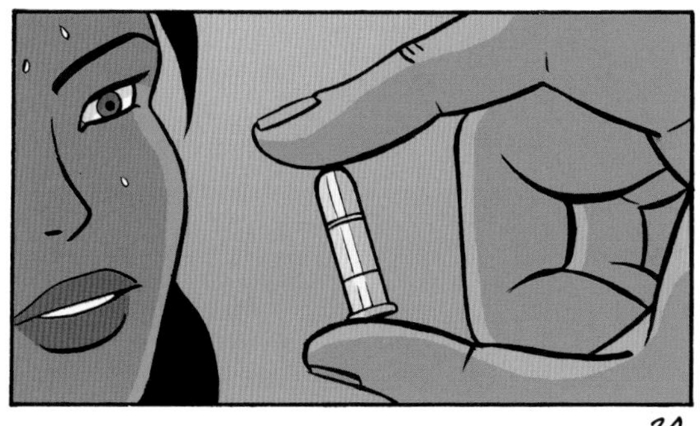

21

ANONYMOUS PHONE CALLS, JACQUES'S STUDIO TRASHED – AND NOW A BULLET!
I CAN'T TAKE ANY MORE OF THIS!
I THINK JACQUES IS RIGHT: CARIMAS HAS GOT A LOT TO LOSE IF THE NEW DIRECTIVE IS APPROVED.

WELL, THEY DON'T KNOW WHO THEY'RE UP AGAINST! I'VE GOT NO INTENTION OF HANDING OUT LICENCES TO POLLUTE!

BUT YOU'RE GOING TO HAVE TO NEGOTIATE WITH THE COUNCIL.

I KNOW.
THEY'VE JUST CONFIRMED THAT THERE WILL BE AN INFORMAL MEETING OF THE CONCILIATION COMMITTEE THIS AFTERNOON. I'M OFF!

MS MARIA CASTANHEIRA, REPRESENTING THE COUNCIL, MR SIMON WEBB, REPRESENTING THE COMMISSION.
HOW DO YOU DO...
...I DON'T THINK MS VEGA, OUR RAPPORTEUR, NEEDS ANY INTRODUCTION!

SO, WHO'S GOING TO FIRE THE OPENING SHOT?
MS VEGA, I SUPPOSE...
LOOK OUT! SHE'S THE PROVERBIAL IRON HAND IN A VELVET GLOVE! HA, HA!
WE'VE BEEN WARNED. HER REPUTATION GOES BEFORE HER!

YOU ARE AWARE THAT WATER IS A SENSITIVE ISSUE AND THE MEMBER STATES' OPINIONS ARE DIVIDED...

...YOU WON'T GET MANY OF THE MEMBER STATES TO AGREE IF YOU DON'T MAKE CONCESSIONS ON IMPLEMENTING DEADLINES AND EXEMPTIONS...

AND THE COMMISSION WON'T HAVE TIME TO DRAW UP THE LIST OF DANGEROUS SUBSTANCES YOU WANT BY THE 1ST OF JULY.

WHAT ARE YOU OFFERING IN EXCHANGE?
THE COUNCIL'S AGREEMENT TO THE REST OF THE AMENDMENTS.

WE'LL THINK ABOUT YOUR PROPOSAL.
SO OUR NEXT MEETING WILL BE ON THURSDAY.

CBT 782 B
KXZ 163
?!

WHAT'S GOING ON?

YOU'LL HAVE TO GO THE OTHER WAY, MA'AM. THERE'S A DEMO BLOCKING THE ROAD.
A DEMO?
PEOPLE FROM THE CHEMICAL INDUSTRY.

23

TRiiiiii
TRiiiiiii
TRiiiii
STOP À LA
STOP
DOWN WITH THE GREEN DICTATOR-SHIP!!!

JACQUES? START WITHOUT ME.
I'LL BE A BIT LATE.

AHA! OUR FAVOURITE MEP! YOU WORK TOO HARD, IRINA!

HERE'S TO JACQUES AND HIS HUNT FOR THE POLLUTERS!
SO, JACQUES, WHAT'S THE PLAN?

HANG ON AND I'LL TELL YOU. I GOT THE IDEA FROM THEM.

WE'RE GOING OFF TOMORROW EVENING TO TAKE PHOTO-GRAPHS AT THE CARIMAS FACTORY!
SHH!

CHICKEN TAJINE?

24

FRIDAY. 00.45 AM
SWITCH OFF!

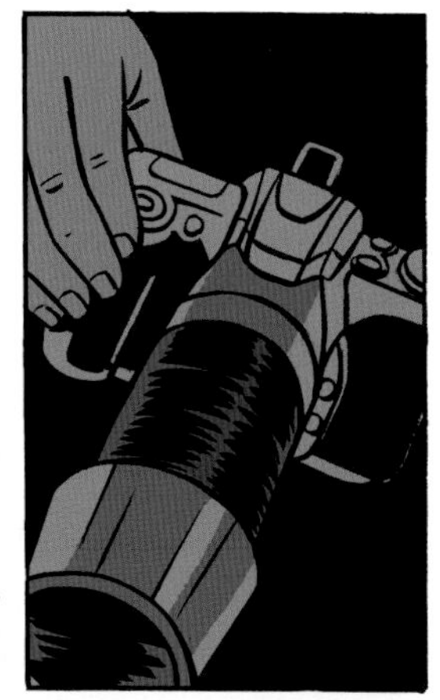

BE CAREFUL! I'LL WAIT FOR YOU IN THE CAR... READY TO GO!

HELLO! WE'VE GOT COMPANY!

TNI-261

QUICK! TURN AROUND! THEY'VE JUST POURED TOXIC WASTE INTO THE RIVER! LET'S GET AFTER THEM!
HPQ-789
IT WAS CARIMAS STUFF, WASN'T IT?

...BARRELS?! DON'T TELL ME...

TNI-261

25

FIMOIL

FIMOIL?!
XST-486

I'VE GOT IT!
LET'S BEAT IT! I DON'T LIKE THIS, JACQUES!
SCREEE

LOOK OUT!
WHAT THE...!! A B***** POTHOLE!

OK, OLD GIRL, LET'S GET OUT OF THIS!
?!

AAAHHHHH

26

TUESDAY. 10 AM
CONCILIATION COMMITTEE
AFTER A GREAT DEAL OF THOUGHT, PARLIAMENT IS WILLING TO ACCEPT THE DEADLINES PROPOSED BY THE COUNCIL. THE MEMBER STATES WILL THEREFORE HAVE TIME TO ADJUST TO THE NEW RULES...

...ON CONDITION THAT THE MEMBER STATES ARE REQUIRED TO TAKE STEPS TO ELIMINATE DANGEROUS SUBSTANCES FROM UNDERGROUND AND SURFACE WATERS AND TO INTRODUCE A FAIR PRICING SYSTEM.
WE CONSIDER PARLIAMENT'S POSITION TO BE REASONABLE.

LADIES AND GENTLEMEN, WE HAVE REACHED AGREEMENT!

SPLENDID! THIS HAS BEEN AN ALL-ROUND SUCCESS.

CONGRATUL-ATIONS ON YOUR NEGOTIATING SKILLS!
HANG ON, IT'S NOT OVER YET!
BEEP BEEP
PARLIAMENT STILL HAS TO APPROVE ...
BEEP BEEP
OH, I'M SORRY... EXCUSE ME!

JACQUES? AT LAST! I DIDN'T KNOW WHAT HAD HAPPENED TO YOU!... HANG ON, I CAN'T HEAR YOU...

27

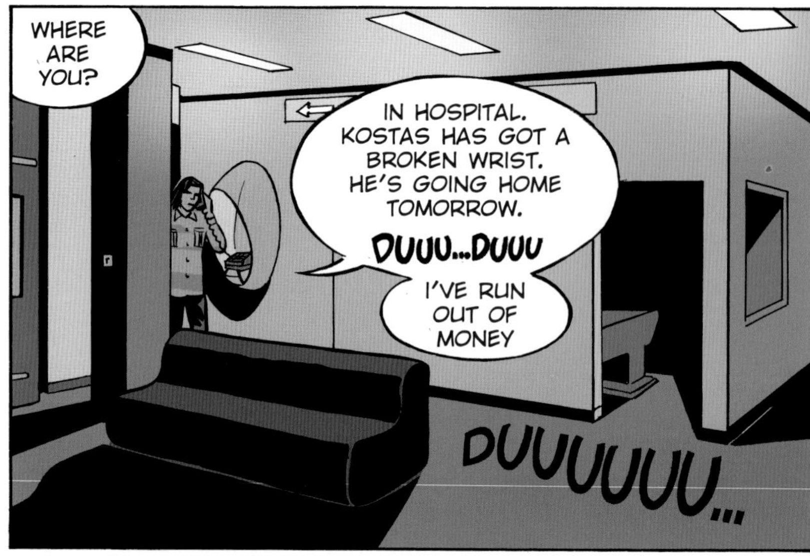

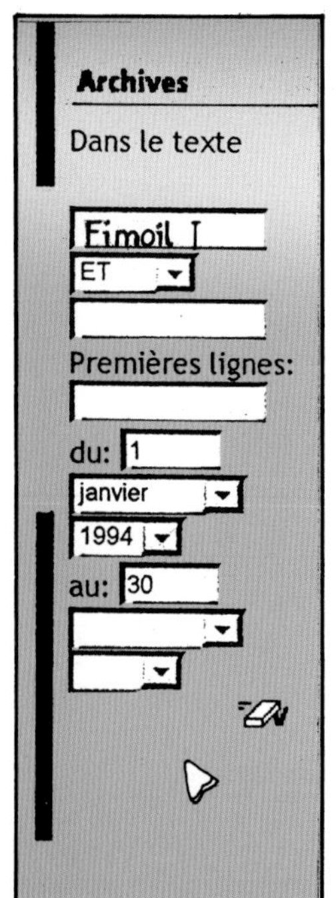

* Fimoil starts price war with Carimas on Asian markets

EDITION SPECIALE
FIMOIL HAS JUST ANNOUNCED A TAKEOVER BID FOR ITS MAIN COMPETITOR, CARIMAS. THIS IS ONE OF THE BIGGEST TAKEOVER BIDS OF THE PAST DECADE...

JACQUES, CAN I COME AND LOOK AT THE FIMOIL PHOTOS? IT'S IMPORTANT. HAVE YOU GOT THEM YET?... I'LL EXPLAIN LATER.

TAXI!

HAVEN'T YOU SEEN THE NEWS?
DON'T TELL ME... I'VE WON A PULITZER PRIZE...

NO, FIMOIL HAS LAUNCHED A TAKEOVER BID FOR CARIMAS.

A TAKEOVER BID!
SO THAT WAS IT! FIMOIL SET UP THE WHOLE THING!

EXACTLY. IT'S ALL FALLING INTO PLACE.

THERE THEY ARE.

THE LEOPARD'S STRATEGY – TIRE YOUR VICTIM OUT AND THEN POLISH HIM OFF...

...AND GET RID OF YOUR WASTE AT THE SAME TIME!

BUT FIMOIL NEVER THOUGHT THEY'D RUN UP AGAINST THE LIKES OF US, EH, IRINA?!

29

WEDNESDAY.
11 AM
MR LOB! AS MANAGING DIRECTOR OF CARIMAS, WHAT IS YOUR REACTION?
ONE WORD ON CARIMAS'S SITUATION?!
LADIES AND GENTLEMEN, PLEASE.
HOTEL

CHRISTIAN LOB
THIS TAKEOVER BID IS THE LAST IN A SERIES OF MOVES MADE AGAINST US BY FIMOIL. THE FUTURE OF THE COMPANY IS NOW IN THE HANDS OF ITS INVESTORS...

... AND TO HELP THEM MAKE THE RIGHT CHOICE, WE HAVE A SURPRISE GUEST ... MR GOLDING ...

FRIDAY, 12.45 AM UNIDENTIFIED MEN EMPTY A NUMBER OF CANS INTO THE RIVER.
TNI-261
THE VAN'S NUMBER PLATE CAN BE SEEN ON THE LEFT.

CARIMAS
THE GATE OF THE CARIMAS FACTORY IS JUST BEHIND IT ...

... A BIT LATER, THE SAME VAN ENTERING FIMOIL'S PREMISES ...
FIMOIL

I AM MAKING ALL MY PHOTOGRAPHS AVAILABLE TO THE PRESS AND THE OFFICIAL INQUIRY.
MR GOLDING!
MR GOLDING!

... THERE HAS BEEN A SPECTACULAR DEVELOPMENT IN THE TOXIC WASTE AFFAIR. THE CHIEF SUSPECT IS NOW FIMOIL.

30

THE FOLLOWING THURSDAY. 9.30 AM STRASBOURG.

I WOULD LIKE TO RECOMMEND THAT PARLIAMENT ADOPT THE OUTCOME OF THE CONCILIATION PROCEDURE. IT WAS NOT AN EASY PROCESS, AND I CONGRATULATE MS VEGA ON HER SKILL IN OBTAINING THE AGREEMENT OF ALL THE POLITICAL GROUPS...
553
477
478

... THIS DIRECTIVE IS THE RESULT OF A COMPROMISE WHICH WILL ENABLE EUROPEAN CITIZENS EVERYWHERE TO ENJOY CLEAN WATER AT A FAIR PRICE.

CLAP!
362
363
CLAP!
CLAP!
CLAP!
CLAP!
THE DEBATE IS OVER. WE SHALL NOW VOTE.

THE WATER POLICY DIRECTIVE IS HEREBY APPROVED!

LOOK AT PAGE 4. THE TESTS HAVE PROVED THAT THE SUBSTANCES DUMPED IN THE RIVER CAME FROM FIMOIL AND NOT FROM CARIMAS. THE MAN WHO GAVE YOU THE SAMPLES WANTED TO TIP YOU THE WINK. BUT WHY?

YES, WHY? AND WHO? WE MAY NEVER KNOW ... SHALL WE HAVE A BITE TO EAT BEFORE WE GO?

JUST WHAT I WAS GOING TO SUGGE'ST!

31

D'YOU THINK SO?

OH,

SO YOU TWO KNOW EACH OTHER?

NO, NO. IT'S THE FIRST TIME WE'VE MET...

WELL, THEN, ALLOW ME TO INTRODUCE OUR NEW COLLEAGUE, VICTOR CAIN. WE POACHED HIM FROM FIMOIL, ***HA, HA, HA!***

BEWARE OF DOUBLE AGENTS!!

THE END

Your EP phrasebook...

Strasbourg
Strasbourg is the seat of the **European Parliament.**

The European Union
The European Union is an ever closer union between the nations of Europe. Its Member States fly their flags in Strasbourg. The fifteen Member States – soon to be more – adopt common policies and measures, because they can achieve better results together than they could individually.

Plenary
The **European Parliament** meets 'in plenary sitting' when it holds its part-sessions – 12 week-long part-sessions in Strasbourg and a number of shorter ones in Brussels. All Members of the European Parliament are expected to attend. When a parliamentary standing **committee** meets, on the other hand, usually only the members of that committee attend.

'If I don't manage to win Parliament over we shall have missed a wonderful opportunity to use our environmental powers...'
The European Parliament, which MEP Irina Vega here refers to as 'Parliament', is elected every five years by the citizens (over 18 years) of the Member States of the **European Union.** At present the European Parliament has 626 Members.
The **Council of Ministers** and the **European Parliament** now adopt European environmental and other 'laws' together. The **directive** on water policy was the first piece of legislation where the European Parliament used **'codecision'** in the area of the environment.

Alex
Members of the European Parliament have parliamentary assistants. Alex is Irina Vega's assistant.

Political group
Like political parties in national parliaments, political groups play a major role in the **European Parliament's** policy decisions. The vast majority of Members of the European Parliament belong to a political group, the others being referred to as 'non-attached' Members. The political groups in the **European Parliament** are made up of Members from different Member States.

Rapporteur
When a parliamentary standing committee has to consider a proposal for a 'European law', it chooses one of its members – the rapporteur – to draw up a report which, if adopted by the committee, is debated and voted on in **plenary**. Once approved, this report constitutes the position of the European Parliament.

Environment Committee
Members of the European Parliament are divided among 17 parliamentary standing committees; the Environment Committee is one of them.

Amendements
An amendment is a change to the proposed text of a law. Amendments are tabled and voted on, first in **committee**, then in the **European Parliament** meeting in **plenary sitting**.

Commission
The European Commission (here referred to simply as 'the Commission') is the institution which initiates 'Community laws', manages European policies and enforces the treaties. At present it is made up of 20 independent Commissioners (2 each from France, Germany, Italy, Spain and the United Kingdom and 1 from each of the other Member States). The Commission is nominated by the governments of the Member States and appointed or rejected by the European **Parliament**.

'El agua no es un bien...'
The work of the interpreters allows parliamentary proceedings to take place in all the official languages of the **European Union**.

Codecision
'Codecision' is the usual legislative procedure of the **European Union:** the **Council of Ministers** and the **European Parliament,** on an equal footing, jointly adopt the 'European laws' proposed by the **European Commission**. The **European Parliament** has to give its final consent.

Council of Ministers
The Council of Ministers – officially called the 'Council of the European Union' – is made up of ministers from each Member State (or their representatives). It adopts 'European laws', often in codecision with the **European Parliament**. Its make-up varies according to the subject (foreign affairs, the budget, the environment etc.).
It should not be confused with the European Council. At least twice a year the European Council – i.e. the heads of state or government of the Member States and the President of the **European Commission** – meets to decide on the main lines of the **European Union**'s policy. The media sometimes refer to these meetings as summits.

'Ladies and gentlemen, we shall now vote!'
The European Parliament sitting in plenary is voting at first reading on the report on the 'proposed law' presented by the European Commission. The codecision process has really begun. It can involve up to three readings by Parliament.

'Ladies and gentlemen...'
While the **European Parliament** is elected for five years, its President is elected by the Members for two and half years, i.e. half a parliamentary term. The President of the **European Parliament** oversees all **Parliament**'s activities, chairs its sittings and represents it in all its external relations.

Common position
The legislative text on which the Council of Ministers agrees after the **European Parliament** has adopted its position at first reading is called a 'common position'.

'Bruxelles-Gare du Luxembourg'
The Gare du Luxembourg is next to the **European Parliament** buildings in Brussels.

'I seem to spend my whole life on the train between Brussels and Strasbourg...'
Members of the European Parliament work in both Strasbourg, where most parliamentary sittings are held, and Brussels, where the standing **committees** and **political groups** hold their meetings and a few additional part-sessions take place. The secretariat of the **European Parliament** is located in a third city, Luxembourg. A number of officials and the staff of the political groups are located in Brussels.

Info Point
There are many **European Union** 'Info Points' in the Member States, as well as in the applicant countries. They provide information for the public on the **European Union** and its policies. The **European Parliament**'s website gives information on the activities of the **European Parliament** and its Members: www.europarl.eu.int.

OSCE
The Organisation for Security and Cooperation in Europe is made up of European, Asian and North American nations. Its role is to prevent conflict situations in Europe, manage them if they do occur and act in the wake of any conflict.

Directive
A directive is one of the forms that a 'European law' can take. It lays down the results to be achieved but leaves it up to the Member States to decide how to achieve them.

Second reading
When the **European Parliament** has received the Council's 'common position' it begins to prepare for its second reading if it wishes to insist on changes proposed at first reading.

NGO
Non-governmental organisation: many organisations that do not depend on governments are active in areas such as food aid, health, human rights and the environment. The list is extremely long, and includes the Red Cross, Amnesty International, Médecins sans Frontières, Caritas, Oxfam and WWF International.

Conciliation Committee
Under the codecision procedure, if there is still disagreement between the **European Parliament** and the **Council of Ministers** after Parliament's second reading, the members of the **Council** and a delegation from **Parliament** meet in a 'Conciliation Committee' to try to find a compromise. The **Parliament** and **Council** delegations are of equal size.

Minority union
Trade unions, which defend the rights of workers in a company, an industry or at national or **European Union** level, first came into being in the nineteenth century. Union elections are held within companies. A union may have a majority or dominant position, or a minority position.

Board
The board of a company is the body which takes strategic decisions for the company.

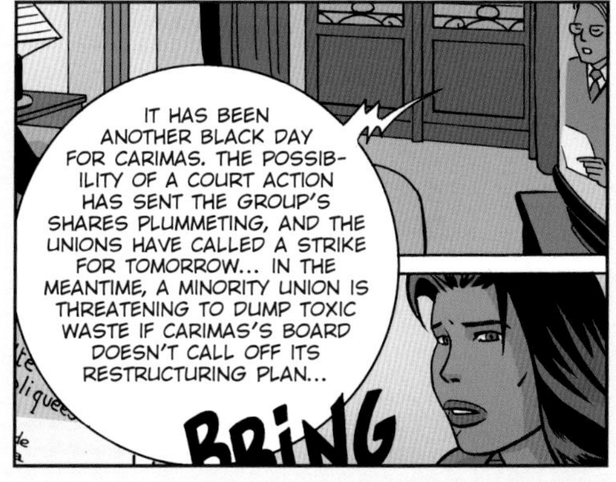

'But you're going to have to negotiate with the Council.'
The **Conciliation Committee** is the forum for this negotiation, the aim of which is to reach a compromise between the **European Parliament** and the **Council** of the European Union.

An informal meeting of the Conciliation Committee
Informal meetings of a **Conciliation Committee** can be held without the presence of all the parties involved. They are preparatory working meetings where, among other things, possible compromise solutions can be discussed.

'Ms Maria Castanheira, representing the Council, Mr Simon Webb, representing the Commission'
At this informal meeting of the **Conciliation Committee** the **Council of Ministers** is represented by an official from the **Member State** holding the Council presidency (a presidency lasts for 6 months), the **Commission** by one of its officials.

'You won't get many of the Member States to agree...'
The Member States adopt a position through the intermediary of their representative on the **Council of Ministers**.

Implementing deadlines
Directives stipulate that the measures adopted must be implemented within a certain period, thus giving the Member States time to adjust.

Conciliation Committee (continued)
At official meetings of a **Conciliation Committee** the **Council of Ministers** presidency is represented by the relevant minister of the country holding the presidency and the **European Commission** is represented by a Commissioner. The **European Parliament** delegation, which is politically balanced, is chaired by one of Parliament's Vice-Presidents and must include the **rapporteur** and the chairman of the relevant parliamentary standing **committee**.

'Parliament still has to approve...'
While success in the conciliation process almost always guarantees the success of the legislative procedure, the **European Parliament** still has to confirm the **Conciliation Committee**'s draft text at a third reading.

'Fimoil has launched a hostile takeover bid!'
When companies are trying to take over a competitor they often use the 'takeover bid' technique. The shareholders of the company being targeted are offered a price for their shares which is higher than their price on the stock exchange. If the company believes this operation to be harmful to it, it will call it a 'hostile takeover bid'.